AN INTRODUCTION TO
THE THEORY OF
VIBRATING SYSTEMS

AN INTRODUCTION TO
THE THEORY OF
VIBRATING SYSTEMS

BY

W. G. BICKLEY
EMERITUS PROFESSOR OF MATHEMATICS

AND

A. TALBOT
LECTURER IN MATHEMATICS

IMPERIAL COLLEGE OF SCIENCE AND TECHNOLOGY
UNIVERSITY OF LONDON

OXFORD
AT THE CLARENDON PRESS
1961

Oxford University Press, Amen House, London E.C.4

GLASGOW NEW YORK TORONTO MELBOURNE WELLINGTON
BOMBAY CALCUTTA MADRAS KARACHI KUALA LUMPUR
CAPE TOWN IBADAN NAIROBI ACCRA

PRINTED IN GREAT BRITAIN

PREFACE

THIS book originated in the course of lectures given for many years by one of us (W. G. B.) to the students in the Communications section of the Department of Electrical Engineering at the City and Guilds College, Imperial College of Science and Technology, in their final year. These students were concerned with mechanical vibrations and mechanical wave propagation, as well as with alternating electric currents and electromagnetic wave propagation. The primary aim was, of course, to familiarize these students with the fundamental ideas, principles, and results of the theory of vibrating systems. To do this it is necessary to enter in some detail into the mathematical methods and techniques appropriate to the topics in question, for, without an understanding of these methods and an ability to apply these techniques, only the simplest problems can be tackled with any prospect of their being solved. We have not, therefore, limited the amount of mathematics used: to have done this would have restricted the range of topics to be dealt with. Rather, by making the meaning of the mathematics as clear as possible by closely associating it with the physical background, and by introducing with—we hope—adequate explanation and exemplification, those more advanced techniques whose acquisition is, in the long run, time-saving, we have endeavoured to extend the reader's competence in mathematics. Emphasis is, frankly, on theory rather than on practice, but we believe that, in science and technology, failure and inefficiency result from inadequate understanding of theory and principle far more often than from practical engineering difficulties. We also believe that this predominantly theoretical approach should render the book serviceable to a much wider range of engineers, physicists, and applied mathematicians than the audience to whom the original lectures were addressed.

The first five chapters cover the theory of systems with one degree of freedom. In these, energy considerations are introduced at the earliest possible moment, partly for their own sake, and partly to prepare for their use later in the application of Rayleigh's principle to the approximate calculation of vibration pulsatances in more complex systems. In the chapter on transients, we have ventured to introduce the general solution, as a definite integral, of the problem of the response of a system to any prescribed disturbing force.

The equations of motion of systems of several degrees of freedom are much more speedily written down by the use of Lagrange's equations—from the energies—than by the use of equations of motion in terms of Newton's laws directly applied, so that a chapter has been devoted to an elementary account of the derivation and use of these equations. They are then applied to the study of systems with multiple freedom, and the pulsatance equation for such systems is constructed. Having solved this equation, the configurations of the normal modes corresponding to the normal pulsatances follow from the equations of motion. The phenomenon of multiple resonance, and the effects of coupling simple systems together, are considered. Since, however, the polynomial pulsatance equation may not be easy to solve for all the roots, and since, in practice, it is often only a few of the slower modes which are of significance, the approximate method which enables the pulsatance of the slowest mode to be determined with high accuracy if the configuration can be guessed approximately, and methods of improving this guess and hence the pulsatance, are of considerable practical value, and have been treated in some detail.

In the original course of lectures the analogies between electrical and mechanical vibrating systems were naturally emphasized wherever possible, and a short chapter giving an account of these analogies has been included.

In continuous systems and media, vibrations are associated with wave propagation, so that, before dealing with the vibrations of finite continuous systems, two chapters on wave propagation have been included. The first of these is general, and the second is devoted to the propagation of sound waves in gases. The propagation of elastic waves in solids was deemed rather too complex to be included. The chapters on the vibrations of finite continuous systems are parallel to those dealing with discrete systems and, again, emphasis is laid on the use of Rayleigh's principle for the approximate calculation of vibration pulsatances.

Finally, an account of some of the important methods of dealing with non-linear systems is attempted. No claim is made, however, that this is more than a very cursory introduction to the subject: a whole book would be needed to give even an outline of the work which has been done in the study of such systems.

Exercises and problems have been appended to most of the chapters. These have been carefully chosen or constructed to give the student the opportunity to test his knowledge and to strengthen it. Relatively few of these exercises, however, involve mere repetition of routine, and nearly all of them are designed to emphasize some additional point. Some of the more difficult imply extensions of the theory given in the text. The exercises include a selection of examination questions on the subject for the B.Sc. (Eng.) degree of the University of London, and these are indicated by (U.L.).

It is our hope that with the range of topics treated here, and the attention we have paid to the exposition and exemplification of the more difficult parts of the subject, this book will be of service to a wide variety of students. For the smaller number who need to enter more deeply into the subject, we should like to hope that a preliminary study of our book will signpost the route, and give the reader such an understanding of fundamentals as will enable him to grapple confidently and successfully with the more advanced treatises devoted to the important range of phenomena associated with vibrating systems.

We are very grateful to the staff of the Clarendon Press for their vigilance, courtesy and ready compliance with our requests.

W. G. B.
A. T.

Imperial College, London
November 1960

CONTENTS

INTRODUCTION xiii

CHAPTER I. FUNDAMENTAL PROPERTIES OF A
    VIBRATING SYSTEM
1.1. Properties essential to a vibrating system 1
1.2. Some simple vibrating systems 2
1.3. Simple harmonic motion 5
1.4. Ubiquity of simple harmonic motion 9
1.5. Determination of pulsatance 10
Appendix 1. Simple spring system 11
Appendix 2. Complex numbers 11
Exercises on Chapter I 14

CHAPTER II. ENERGY IN VIBRATING SYSTEMS
2.1. Kinetic energy 16
2.2. Potential energy 17
2.3. Potential energy (cont.) 19
2.4. From energy to equation of motion 22
2.5. Energy method for the determination of pulsatance 22
2.6. Examples of the energy method 23
Exercises on Chapter II 25

CHAPTER III. DISSIPATION OF ENERGY: DAMPED
    VIBRATIONS
3.1. Laws of friction or resistance: equation of motion 27
3.2. Solution of equation; damped vibrations 29
3.3. Large damping 33
3.4. Critical damping 34
3.5. Dissipation of energy 35
Exercises on Chapter III 36

CHAPTER IV. MAINTAINED VIBRATIONS
4.1. Steady-state vibrations 37
4.2. The equation of motion 37
4.3. Solution of the equation 38
4.4. Meaning of solution: response curves 39
4.5. Some special cases 44
4.6. The electrical analogue 48
4.7. Mechanical impedance; dynamic stiffness 49
4.8. Power supply 50
Exercises on Chapter IV 51

CHAPTER V. TRANSIENTS

5.1. Introduction 53
5.2. General 53
5.3. Undamped system. Simple cases 54
5.4. Damped system. Simple cases 58
5.5. The general disturbing force 61
Exercises on Chapter V 64
Miscellaneous exercises on Chapters I to V 64

CHAPTER VI. LAGRANGE'S EQUATIONS

6.1. Coordinates: degrees of freedom 67
6.2. The energies, and the work differential 70
6.3. Lagrange's equations 73
6.4. Examples of the use of Lagrange's equations 75
Exercises on Chapter VI 80

CHAPTER VII. SYSTEMS WITH SEVERAL DEGREES OF FREEDOM: NORMAL MODES

7.1. Introduction 82
7.2. Pulsatances and amplitude ratios of normal modes 84
7.3. System with three degrees of freedom 86
7.4. Some effects of coupling 90
7.5. Lagrange's pulsatance determinant 92
Exercises on Chapter VII 93

CHAPTER VIII. SYSTEMS WITH SEVERAL DEGREES OF FREEDOM: MAINTAINED VIBRATIONS

8.1. Introduction 96
8.2. Vibration due to an external force 97
8.3. Vibration due to a prescribed motion 99
8.4. The coupling of equal systems; 'double-humped' response curve 101
Exercises on Chapter VIII 103

CHAPTER IX. RAYLEIGH'S PRINCIPLE AND OTHER APPROXIMATE METHODS

9.1. Introduction 106
9.2. A simple example 107
9.3. Some theory 108
9.4. Improvement of the approximation 109
9.5. Successive approximation and iteration 111
9.6. The next mode 113
9.7. A closer approximation 115
Exercises on Chapter IX 116

CHAPTER X. ELECTRO-MECHANICAL ANALOGIES

10.1. Introduction 117
10.2. Connected systems 117
10.3. Some simple examples 118
10.4. Some further remarks 124
Exercises on Chapter X 126

CHAPTER XI. WAVE PROPAGATION

11.1. Introduction 128
11.2. The differential equation of wave propagation 129
11.3. Solutions of the wave equation 132
11.4. Initial and end conditions 133
11.5. Reflection: simple cases 135
11.6. Progressive waves: transmission impedance: energy 139
11.7. Simple harmonic waves 141
11.8. Reflection and transmission 142
Exercises on Chapter XI 147

CHAPTER XII. SOUND

12.1. Introduction 149
12.2. Physical properties of gases and liquids 149
12.3. Plane waves of sound 151
12.4. Sinusoidal sound waves 153
12.5. Atmospheric acoustics 154
12.6. Change of medium: transmission and reflection 155
12.7. Sound waves in three dimensions 156
12.8. Spherical sound waves 158
12.9. Sinusoidally varying source 159
12.10. Propagation along a tube of variable section 160
12.11. The exponential horn 161
Exercises on Chapter XII 161

CHAPTER XIII. SIMPLE FINITE CONTINUOUS SYSTEMS

13.1. Introduction 164
13.2. Transverse vibrations of a taut string 165
13.3. Some other simple systems 168
13.4. More complex systems 170
13.5. Initial conditions 175
13.6. Orthogonality of the normal functions 176
13.7. Expansion in series of normal functions 178
13.8. Examples 179
13.9. Maintained vibrations 181
Exercises on Chapter XIII 182

CHAPTER XIV. VIBRATIONS OF BEAMS AND WHIRLING
OF SHAFTS

14.1. Introduction 185
14.2. Elements of beam theory 185
14.3. Transversely vibrating bars 187
14.4. The pinned-pinned bar 188
14.5. The clamped-free bar 189
14.6. The effect of an added mass 190
14.7. Whirling of shafts 191
14.8. Orthogonality of solutions 192
Exercises on Chapter XIV 193

CHAPTER XV. APPROXIMATE METHODS FOR CONTINUOUS
SYSTEMS

15.1. Introduction 195
15.2. The vibrating taut string 195
15.3. Successive approximation 197
15.4. An extension of Rayleigh's principle 198
15.5. The general case 199
15.6. The taut circular membrane 201
15.7. Beams and shafts 203
15.8. The clamped-free bar 203
Exercises on Chapter XV 204

CHAPTER XVI. NON-LINEAR SYSTEMS

16.1. Introduction 206
16.2. The simple pendulum 207
16.3. The phase plane 209
16.4. A damped system 213
16.5. van der Pol's equation 216
16.6. Periodic vibrations 218
16.7. Maintained vibrations 219
16.8. Sum and difference tones 220
16.9. Energy methods 221
16.10. Slowly varying amplitude and phase 223

ANSWERS 225

BIBLIOGRAPHY 231

INDEX 233

INTRODUCTION

VIBRATIONS and vibrating systems are so common, not only
in engineering and physical science, but in everyday life, that
a general description is unnecessary. It may, however, serve
to emphasize this ubiquity by quoting a number of instances of
such phenomena.

The two senses by which we apprehend the majority of our
external world, sight and hearing, both depend upon vibratory
phenomena. In the case of sound, the vibrations are those of
ordinary materials—vibrations of solids causing vibratory waves
in the air which again cause vibrations of the drum and bones
of the ear, and in the tissue, so stimulating nerve impulses. As
regards sight, although modern advances have restored a 'cor-
puscular' aspect of light, its wave properties are still accepted,
and the association of frequency with colour is maintained.
Radio and X-rays are known to be phenomena of exactly the
same nature as light, differing only in the scale of wavelength
or frequency. Radio is inextricably connected also with electric
circuits and with mechanical vibrations. The frequency of a
transmitter carrier wave is maintained constant by coupling
with a vibrating quartz crystal; the modulation is produced by
mechanical vibrations in a microphone.

But the essential properties of these vibration phenomena,
in which the vibrations are not directly sensed as such, have
much—very much—in common with more obvious vibrations
such as the pendulum, waves on the sea and the consequent
rolling of a boat, swaying of trees in the wind, the cradle and
the rocking-chair, and musical instruments like the harp, drums,
bells (the mechanism of wind instruments is not quite so obvious,
but some of these incorporate a vibrating 'reed').

As regards engineering examples, the mechanical engineer has
many reciprocating engines, but even in non-reciprocating
machinery there may be torsional vibrations in the shafts, and
also transverse vibrations and the closely associated phenomenon

of 'whirling'. Vibrations of turbine disks have caused much serious trouble. In the case of rotating machinery which is out of balance, vibrations of an undesirable or even dangerous nature may be caused in the supports and transmitted through floor or ground to other parts of the building or structure which houses the machine or of which the machine forms part. We may instance also the vibrations of a car or lorry body, or a railway carriage, on its springs. In the aeroplane the problem of unwanted vibration is particularly acute, and even when jet engines and gas turbines remove the periodicities inherent in reciprocating engines, lateral and torsional vibrations of wings, drumming of panels, and the complex set of phenomena known generally as 'flutter' remain. The civil engineer is concerned with vibrations of girder and suspension bridges—troops break step in crossing the latter, the locomotive's 'hammer blow' may strain the former. Problems of noise insulation in buildings, and of minimizing the effects of low-frequency vibrations from machinery or street traffic, may greatly influence methods of construction. Finally, the electrical engineer's alternating currents and voltages are described in the same mathematical language as, and are completely analogous to, mechanical vibrations; the analogy is much more important theoretically than practically, although important mechanical vibrations may be electrically maintained. The behaviour of a mechanical system which is analogous to an electrical network may often be readily visualized. More important still, the techniques, concepts, and nomenclature introduced or invented with reference to alternating currents have been taken over into the treatment of mechanical and acoustical vibrations with considerable profit.

The succeeding chapters attempt to analyse the principles which underlie all these diverse problems, and, by formulating them mathematically, to show how much is in essence common to them all. By solving the equations presented by this mathematical formulation, the behaviour of the systems is deduced, and general rules emerge whereby the ill effects of unwanted vibrations can be diminished or the wanted effects enhanced.

FUNDAMENTAL PROPERTIES OF A VIBRATING SYSTEM

1.1. Properties essential to a vibrating system

OUR first task must be to discover, by careful examination of some typical vibrating systems, those properties of such systems which are essential properties in the absence of which vibration phenomena do not occur.

Perhaps the most important property of systems which are capable of vibrating is that they *need not* vibrate. A pendulum need not swing, musical instruments can remain dumb, a shaft with pulleys or a flywheel attached can remain at rest, or rotate uniformly without exhibiting any torsional oscillations, and similar statements are found to hold true for other systems. It therefore appears that one property essential to a vibrating system is the existence of a *position of equilibrium*.

It is not until the body is disturbed, or displaced from its equilibrium position, that it can exhibit vibrational characteristics, and if it is to do so, the effect of any displacement must be to produce a *restoring* force. Alternatively stated, this means that the equilibrium must be *stable*. Vibrations occur about a position or configuration of stable equilibrium.

It is worth while to emphasize at this early stage that the possession of a position of equilibrium affords a natural, intrinsic, datum from which to measure the displacement of the system when in motion, and that in terms of the displacement so measured from the position of equilibrium, any quantity or equation pertaining to the system will be expressed in the simplest possible manner.

There is a second essential property also. When a system capable of vibrating is displaced from the equilibrium position and let go, the restoring force causes it to move towards the equilibrium position. A vibration will, however, not ensue unless the system, on its return, 'overshoots the mark', that is, passes through and beyond the equilibrium position. The general property of matter which makes it tend to go on moving when once on the move is called *inertia*, and we see that in order to be able to vibrate, a system *must possess inertia*—or something equivalent.

In addition to these two positive requirements, there is also a negative requirement which must be fulfilled if a system is to be capable of executing free vibrations. Its necessity may be seen by imagining a pendulum suspended in thick oil. Restoring force and inertia are still present, but the friction may be sufficient to prevent the bob from doing more than returning very slowly to the equilibrium position, without 'overshooting the mark'. The third essential requirement is, therefore, that *friction* (or its equivalent) *shall not be too great*. How great it may be is a question of its magnitude relative to other quantities inherent in the system, and this will be investigated in Chapter III.

Meanwhile it must be recognized that in many systems the effects of friction are very small. For example, in laboratory experiments to determine the relation between the length and period of a simple pendulum, with a leaden bob suspended by a fine cotton, it is possible to count several hundred swings. The slow rate of decay in this and in similar cases shows that the effects of friction are often so small that they may justifiably be omitted, at least to obtain a first approximation in cases where they are known to be small. Complete justification for this will be given in Chapter III, but in this and the next chapter we shall neglect the effects of friction.

1.2. Some simple vibrating systems

Perhaps the simplest instance, and one which we shall regard as typical, of a vibrating system is that of a mass controlled by a light spring (Fig. 1). Let m be the mass, and s be the stiffness (i.e. the restoring force per unit displacement, taken to be a constant) of the spring, and let x be the displacement of m from its *equilibrium* position at any time. Then the restoring force is sx.